BODY BUILDER

A PHOTOGRAPHIC PERSPECTIVE

By Parham Donyai
LL.B.(Hons), Dip. LP, MCSR, ITEC

A JOURNEY INTO A SPECIAL WORLD

I started first photographing body builders around 1998. This was by accident really. As I got involved with the body building industry, I found myself in various happening places (well, in terms of body building anyway!).

In my time, I have photographed many different physiques from small physiques of up and coming body builders to people like Ronnie Coleman, Jay Cutler, Lenda Murray and so on. I have attended many shows such as The Olympia, The Arnold Classic, NPC shows, Musclemania, BNBF, NPA, IFBB and EFBB shows. I have also had private shooting sessions with many top body builders. This book is a collection of some favourite photographs from around 1998 up to 2005. They have caught various male and female physiques at different angles, in different lights and at different times.

This book is published as an inspiration to all those aspiring body builders, those struggling to lose fat, gain muscle, get back into shape, those being bullied, getting frustrated, growing a belly, getting ready for contests, thinking of competing, looking back at their competitive lives and anybody and everybody who was, is or will be interested in body building.

Body building is a great sport and often misconstrued. I hope these following pages will serve as a positive comment on what is a big part of mine and many people's life.

Life never stops. A photograph capturing a moment is history a moment later. This book is a collection of various moments. Enjoy!

PAUL LA PIAZZA, AMATEUR BODY BUILDER, PERSONAL TRAINER

WHO IS A BODY BUILDER?

One of the greatest misconceptions about body builders is that they are dumb. I disagree with this. I don't disagree with it because I am a dumb body builder myself. I disagree because I have known many body builders and a great proportion of them are actually very intelligent. This especially goes for competitive body builders.

Think about it. You cannot be stupid, if you know how to go from 20% body fat to 5% body fat in 4-6 weeks. You will need to know about exercises, different foods, diets, food combinations, supplements and various other contributory factors such as sleep, stress, insulin, thermogenics, diuretics and so on. Sounds easy? I didn't think so!

A body builder is someone who loves lifting weights, seeing themselves get bigger, feeling the weights, the lifting, the lowering, the stretching, the contractions, the pump. A competitive body builder is a sculptor, a person on a mission.

I agree that some body builders are insecure from within and body build to feel better and become more confident. This may seem like a weakness but surely it is more preferential to lift weights than use alcohol or drugs to overcome emotional inadequacies.

To the general public, a body builder is a big man or woman that lifts weights. To someone who knows, there are two distinct types of body builders. Those who are natural and use many foods and supplements to get as big and/or as lean as possible and those who use any means including anabolic steroids to get as big and/or lean as possible.

Natural and steroid using body builders are usually miles apart in thought and appearance. The huge monsters you see in magazines and in the media are steroid-using body builders. The smaller physiques usually belong to natural body builders.

All muscle-bound physiques can be beautiful, for it has taken hours of gym work, lots of food and possibly other aides to develop a body builder's physique. This book pays homage to the body builder and makes no distinction between natural or steroid using, man or woman. They are all body builders and share one common bond deep down, their love of iron.

MARK CAMERON AND JAMIE CAMERON (NOT RELATED!)

PERSONAL EXPERIENCES
WITH BODY BUILDERS

Though this book is a collection of photographs, I feel that it cannot be complete without at least a few personal words. These are from the heart and meant to give you a more intimate and real feel about the world which I have experienced.

I am always surprised when I speak to body builders. I actually make it a point of speaking to as many body builders as I can because not one is the same as the other.

One of the greatest body builders this country has ever seen was a personal hero of mine… well, until I got to speak with him. This man was a complete contradiction to my earlier defence of the dumb body builder. I will give you a rough example of the first (and last) conversation I ever had with him:

"Hi, I have read a lot about you and thought I'd just say hello," I said to the great one.

"Hi, where have you come up from today?" he said.

"Oh, we came up from London, from xxx company to see the show."

"Great, you guys are a gym, right?"

"No, we are not, just a sports company in London."

"Oh in London? Whereabouts in London?"

"West London."

"Great, great, so you have a gym, right?"

"Umm, no. It's a sports company."

"Great. Whereabouts in London?"

"Errr, WEST LONDON."

"Where is west London?"

"Ummm… TO THE WEST OF LONDON."

I made a quick exit at this point.

This was probably one of my less memorable (I did try to forget it many times!) experiences. Another negative experience of mine which has stuck in my mind goes back to Rome a few years ago. I had bumped into one of the major US stars of body building in a hotel lobby and thought it would be good to have a photo of him as he was promoting his appearance there.

He asked for money to take his photo, which was sort of unusual for a pro in a hotel lobby! I said that I didn't have any cash on me and he asked to take my credit card number.

These are the bad examples. The good examples are plenty and I am quite lucky to consider many of the top UK body builders my personal friends. They really are a great bunch of people and I truly respect them for the effort and dedication they put into their body building.

Most body builders have full time jobs, spouses, children, commitments, money restraints and daily stress. Yet they manage to build beautiful, flawless physiques. When you look at them and see how goal-oriented, persistent, dedicated and hard-working they are, it makes you think twice about your own pathetic excuses for not getting things done.

None of the physiques in this book have been created overnight or without hard work. These body builders have trained hard, paid attention to their diet, used supplements and excelled in their sport.

PAUL BEING PICKED UP, NOTHING UNUSUAL
AS MEN AND WOMEN ADORE HIM

AGGI DULSON

VICKY MCCANN, NATURAL BODY BUILDER

ROB RICHES, BODY BUILDER AND MALE MODEL

WHAT IS A GREAT BODY?

Everyone will have their own definition of this. Sitting as a spectator in a body building competition you will always hear different people in the crowd express various opinions about the physiques on stage.

A great body is invariably one with the full package, size, symmetry, great upper body, great legs, low body fat. One thing you will find the common denominator in the photos in this book and what sets these people apart from others is "the ability to pose".

The ability to pose is the differentiating factor between a body builder and a weight trainer. A body builder is aware of his or her muscles and knows how to flex them. A great body builder looks great in any light, whether they are flexing or not. Why? Because even when they look like they are not flexing, they actually are. They are always aware of their various muscles and know how to show them off in the best light, whether at full contraction or seemingly relaxed.

This is why I think posing in front of a mirror is an integral part of every body builder's life and an absolute must for success. Many natural body builders don't even look like body builders with their clothes on, but they are masters of making their muscles look ten times the size they really are.

A great body is one which looks absolutely flawless from at least one angle. If it looks great from other angles, then that's a bonus. Before photographing people in photo-shoots, I always try and do a complete study of their physique to get the best out of them.

Many great physiques may not have the complete package. Some body builders are known for their lagging parts or their overdeveloped ones. Either way, a great body is one which can look awesome in at least one particular light/angle.

BODY BEAUTIFUL

AYMAR, ONE OF THE MOST REQUESTED PHOTOS! PEOPLE CAN'T GET ENOUGH OF THIS PICTURE AND MANY HAVE CLASSIFIED IT AS THEIR IDEAL LOOK

INTIMATE TRAINING SESSION IN ONE OF LONDON'S MOST HARDCORE GYMS, GENESIS

FAME COMPETITOR, USA 2004

NAV 'SWORD' MASHAN, EFBB & NABBA COMPETITOR

POWER MACHINES

LAUNDER PHILOGENE

SWORD FLEXING HIS BICEPS

TANNING THE BODY

THE SWORD, 2 WEEKS AFTER COMPETITION
HAVING CARBED UP AGAIN

SWORD

PROTECT

HUSSEIN, PERSIAN WRESTLING CHAMPION
AND NATURAL BODY BUILDER

THE HULK

NEVER TOO OLD!

MUSCLEMANIA CHAMPION

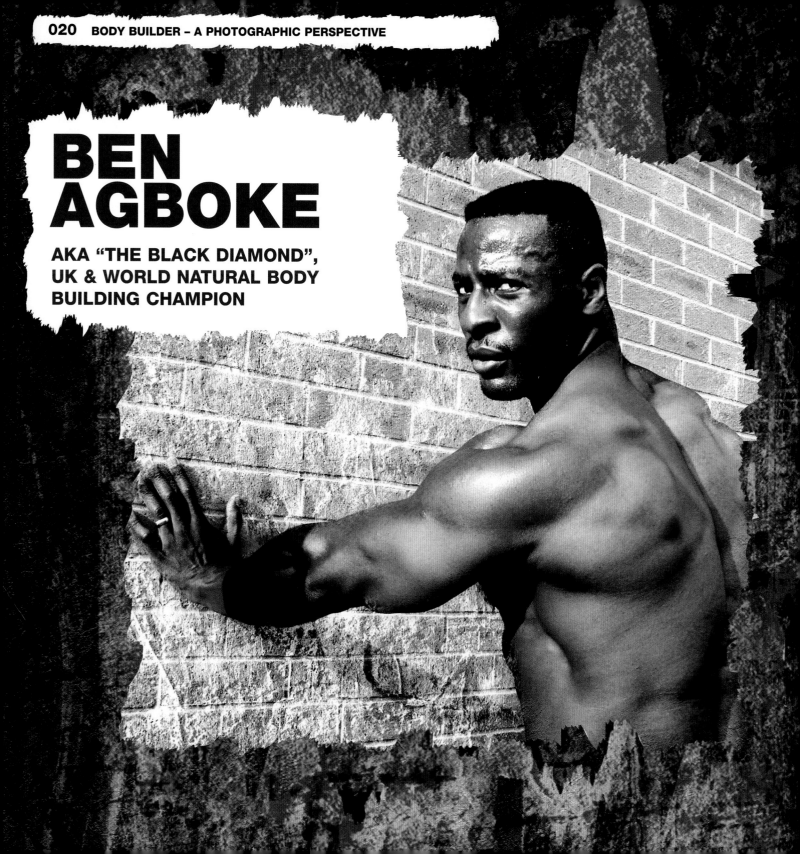

BEN AGBOKE

AKA "THE BLACK DIAMOND", UK & WORLD NATURAL BODY BUILDING CHAMPION

I have known Ben for over 7 years. As someone who knows him well, I know that he is a 100% natural body builder. Many people find this hard to believe as they just cannot envisage someone being 18.5 stones off season and still natural.

I can understand their scepticism as I had similar thoughts upon seeing people like Rob Feesey. How can this man be natural and have such an astonishing physique? The fact is that these people are natural and you have to take their word for it.

PUMPING UP BACKSTAGE AT MUSCLEMANIA

Ben went from being an aspiring body builder with a good physique to the UK and then World Body Building Champion, all in the space of a few short years. Ben's mind is a strong mind that believes he can achieve anything.

Ben Agboke is a man who has been at the height of his sport and achieved more than most body builders. He is intelligent, articulate and runs a thriving business alongside his sport. He is a great example to body building and body builders and a man of admirable principles.

Despite temptations, he has remained true to his sport as a natural body builder and has competed against people who use all manners of drugs to gain an advantage and he has still held his own amongst them. To Ben, body building is about a way of life and if you change this way of life, you change the very essence of who you are.

I have photographed Ben since 1998 and have seen some dramatic changes in his physique. Ben has absolutely amazing leg development, with huge arms and is extremely strong for a natural body builder.

You can see that Ben trains like a power-lifter as well as a body builder because he has thickness in his muscles. Off season, Ben can look like a mass monster, but come competition time, he has a small waist and absolutely chiselled mid-section.

**BEN AGBOKE, PAUL AMOS AND JAMIE CAMERON
AT THE EFBB 2003 (JAMIE NOT COMPETING)**

THE BLACK DIAMOND

BEN AGBOKE AND HIS BEAUTIFUL WIFE JENNIFER

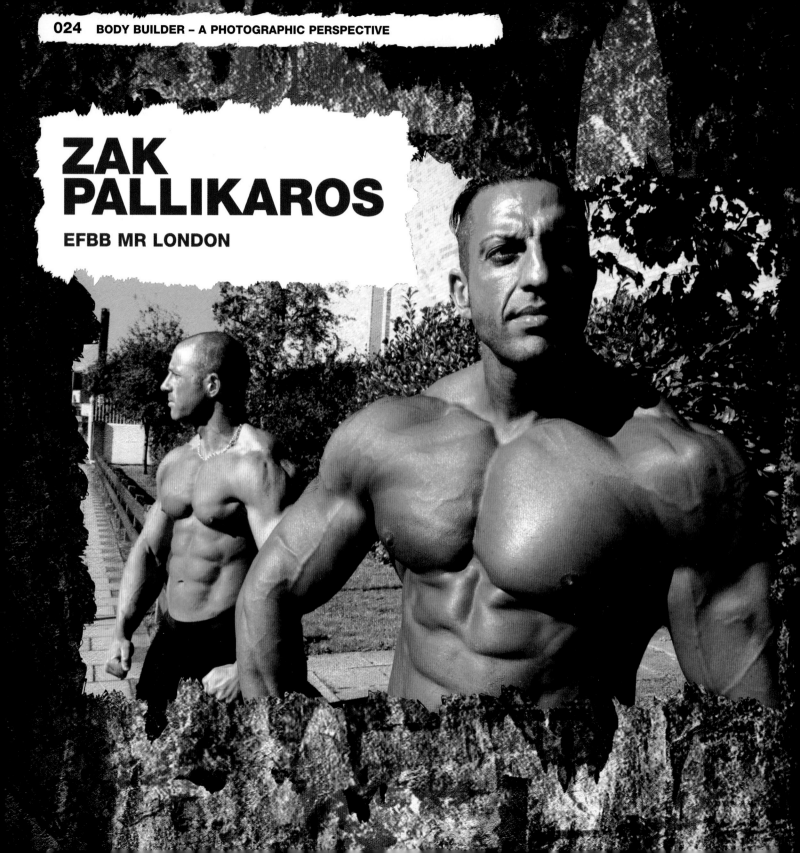

ZAK PALLIKAROS

EFBB MR LONDON

One of my most favourite people to photograph is Zak Pallikaros. He is a natural poseur and knows his body very well. He is always in top shape and looks pretty good from most angles.

I first saw Zak at an EFBB qualifier in London and thought he looked amazing. He was by far in the best condition out of all other competitors. He looked big, ripped and MEAN!

Zak may be many things but mean he is not! He is one of the nicest and most gentle people I have come across. His exterior is very deceptive. He is a very intelligent and articulate man with a great heart. Here is a little run-down on Zak in his own words.

DR. ZAK PALLIKAROS DOB: 6/4 1970

I started competing in bodybuilding in 1999
Contest History Includes:

1999 Tower Gym show: 1st Place in Over 21 class and won overall Mr Tower Gym

2000 Tower Gym show: 1st Place in Over 21 class and won overall Mr Tower Gym

2002 EFBB London and South East: 1st place in 1st timers class and also won Best Poser award

2002 EFBB Mr Britain: 3rd place in 1st timers class

2004 EFBB London and South East: 1st place in Intermediate class

2004 EFBB Mr Britain: 2nd place in Intermediate class over 80kg

2004 Mr Cyprus: 2nd place in the under 90kg class

2004 IFBB Amateur British Grand Prix Invitational: 6th Place

WORKING AND BODY BUILDING AT THE SAME TIME

I am currently working for GE Healthcare (previously known as Amersham Plc). It's now the largest worldwide Healthcare Company. My position is Team Leader in a research laboratory specialising in research and development in drug therapy. I have a first class honours degree in Medicinal Chemistry and a Doctorate in Steroid Biochemistry obtained at the Royal Free hospital.

It's very hard to keep a full time responsible Job as well and bodybuilding. My love for the sport makes it possible to fit in the workouts, the preparation of meals and what's required to be a competitive bodybuilder. For example, 3 months before a competition, I would wake up at 5am and do 30 min cardio on my stationary bike at home, then get ready for work.

I start work at 8am (I have a 35 mile journey to work on the M25). I get home around 6pm, get ready to go Gym and do my weights workout, finish and go home and prepare my meals for the next day. That's the only way to fit everything in. When you achieve that competitive look you want and the minute you step on stage, all the hard work is forgotten and it makes it all worth while. Those few minutes on stage are worth everything to me!

I always admired strong people and my family name (Pallikaros) in Greek actually means "Strong Man" which after tracing back my family history discovered that my great grandfather was the strongest man in his town and his achievements are still talked about.

CHECKING OUT THE COMPETITION

I was always into martial arts and as a young boy idolised Bruce Lee, having done Karate and Judo for about 6 years I then did Kung-Fu for 3-4 years then finally I set up a small gym in my parents garage (with posters of Arnold and Franco all over the walls) and would work out with weights every night whilst studying for my "O" and "A" levels. My introduction to proper Bodybuilding came from my cousin George Michael (not the singer). He was a competitive bodybuilder himself when I was a skinny 18 year old. I always looked up to him and he was the first person to take me to a proper Hardcore Gym (the Tower Gym) where I still train now. The rest is History!

Bodybuilding has helped me in almost every part of my life. I believe I am a more confident person, I've made loads of friends through the sport, and for me I find going to the gym is the best way to beat everyday stress. Exercise is the best thing for the mind as well as the body. I feel relaxed and content after a good workout. My diet is clean and healthy, I take the correct supplements and vitamins, I take care of my body and appearance and when compared to people my age (that don't train) I look and feel 10 years younger than them.

INSPIRATIONS

What inspires me mainly is myself. The gains I make, the comments I get from people, I basically try to improve all the time. I am never satisfied with the way I look and always try to better myself. A big inspiration is when coming up to a show and you see the transformation your body goes from losing the fat and becoming a lean machine on stage with the 6-pack and the shredded muscles. To me that's what inspires me and the love and enjoyment I get from the sport keeps me motivated. I am also a bit of a perfectionist and in whatever I do I have to give it 110% in order to be happy. For that reason I work extremely hard in whatever I set my mind. I set realistic goals to myself and don't rest until I achieve them then move onto the next bigger goal. I am always in competition with myself and try to improve. I love bodybuilding because it's an individual sport and you don't have to rely on other people like team sports. Basically what you put in, you get out! This is also the only sport that you carry the results everywhere you go with you, even to the grave! My biggest inspiration in Bodybuilding is Arnold and his "Stay Hungry" Philosophy! My biggest inspiration in life are my parents and son!

IFBB STAGE

POWERFUL MAN, NEXT TO A VERY POWERFUL MACHINE. THIS PHOTO HAS AN EIGHTIES FEEL ABOUT IT AND WAS USED ON THE COVER OF A WELL-KNOWN FLAPJACK

BEST EXERCISES

For Chest, I believe the King exercise is the bench press (both inclined and flat)

For Back I would have to say weighted-chin ups

For legs with no doubt the Squats

For shoulders press behind the neck

For biceps standing barbell curls and for triceps lying triceps extensions with EZ bar.

These are the basic exercises I believe for Mass building. Hardcore but effective. Nearer a show you start doing more shaping exercises such as lunges and leg extensions, concentration curls, triceps push downs, lateral raises etc... you sculpt your body like an artist and work on the weaker body-parts.

DIETING

The main preparation for a competition is the diet which I pay a lot of attention to as I believe that Diet is 70% of bodybuilding. With diet I also mean the supplementation that's almost impossible to get in that condition without supplements. Having a PhD in biochemistry, I am very selective in what supplements I take in terms of Nutritional value and above all quality. After doing my research I now stick with one brand that I am very happy with hence my sponsorship with LA Muscle. The look I achieve in my shows is always talked about by my fellow competitors and spectators. I always get asked questions how I achieve my condition and I simply put it down to diet, supplements, hard work and determination as well as genetics (thanks Mum and Dad!)

BEST MEMORY

My best moment I guess has to be the 2002 EFBB Mr London and South East when I won my class as well as winning best poser award for the overall show! What an amazing day that was! I posed to superman music and up to this date I go to shows and people still call me Super-Zak hence the tattoo on my left shoulder with a Z in a superman sign! My most special and precious moment I will never forget though has to be my first show. Winning Mr Tower Gym and Overall Mr Tower Gym, then my son Nicholas then 3 years old coming up on stage to lift the trophy with me. Up to this date I look at that Photo and I can see on his face how proud he looks for me winning and I look even more proud having him there to share my first ever victory on stage. Even up to this day he takes the magazine with my photos to school to show his friends and teachers and I feel like a celebrity going to his parents' evenings and school plays!

My favourite exercise is the bench press for chest and squats for legs. I love the pump you get from these basic mass building exercises.

I now get a lot of pleasure in helping other people in the gym both young and old, men and women with their training and nutrition. My approachable nature makes it easy for them to talk to me and I feel good when I see them making improvements and being satisfied with their results. For this reason I am now doing a personal training course that covers nutrition etc to use that in a more greater extend.

TAKEN IN 2004

ZAK, A SHADOWY FIGURE, SCULPTED USING
TRAINING, DIET AND SUPPLEMENTS

Finally Like everything else in life nothing can be achieved without the support and love of your Parents. In my case, they have been behind me 110% in everything I do, academically as well as in my bodybuilding. To them, I owe everything I have done and the person I am today!

Most frequent question I get from people is about my Job, they find it hard to believe what I do for a living as everyone stereotypically classes bodybuilders as not very intelligent muscleheads, well, I, as well as hundreds of other bodybuilders out there prove that wrong. There's more to the exterior hard surface that people see. In my experience I have met a lot of intelligent bodybuilders whose knowledge about nutrition and the function of the human body is amazing. Also believe it or not some of the most kind-hearted sensitive people I know are bodybuilders! Never judge a book by its cover!!

AT THE 2004 EFBB BRITISH FINALS

KERRY NAPIER

2004 NATURAL OVERALL BRITISH BODY BUILDING CHAMPION

Kerry is one of those people that seems to have come from nowhere to become the talk of the natural body building scene. He has an amazing body and great conditioning. Here is Kerry in his own (very honest) words!

My name is Kerry Napier, I am 29 years old. I have only been competing for a year and in that time I was lucky enough to win the British Natural Bodybuilding Federations Overall British Title which won me my pro card, allowing me to compete in WNBF shows in the United States.

I currently work as a Personal Trainer/Fitness Instructor for a local gym. Due to the fact that I work at a gym it's fairly easy for me to mix my Bodybuilding and work, so no problems there.

I don't have any of the clichéd reasons for taking up Bodybuilding. I came into some money and promptly blew the lot, however I did buy a set of weights during my spending spree. Started working out and the rest is history.

I wouldn't say body building has been a great help to me. Obviously being well built helped me with the ladies when I was younger but beyond the benefits of being healthier, it's not helped me much. In truth it has cost me an absolute fortune.

I find staying motivated very difficult. Other Bodybuilders don't inspire me so my motivation comes purely from myself. I haven't missed a workout yet but the older I'm getting I can sense that day is going to come along sooner rather than later.

2004 BNBF OVERALL CHAMPION

MY FAVOURITE EXERCISES ARE AS FOLLOWS:

Chest: Smith Machine Incline Presses.

Back: Deadlifts.

Legs: Squats.

Biceps: Alternate Dumbbell Curls.

Triceps: Two Arm Dumbbell Extensions.

Shoulders: Smith Machine Military Presses.

I get in shape for contests over a 10 week period. I stay lean all year round so contest prep is fairly easy. I just cut my carbs and up my Protein intake. I do Cardio all year round but I may throw in an extra session now and then as the show approaches. I do get pretty hungry by the end but I never cheat on my diet. I think how stupid I'd look standing onstage if I was out of shape and that stops me cheating.

The highlight of my Bodybuilding career so far has to be winning the Overall Title at the British Final in my first year of competing. I don't think anything will be able to compare to that feeling.

My favourite exercise has to be Deadlifts. I am pretty strong at these and I feel that consistent Deadlifting is the reason for my physique reaching the standard it has.

As much as I love Bodybuilding, the discipline required to succeed is immense and it's probably something best avoided in your teens and early 20's. Sure lift weights but make sure you also enjoy your life as well e.g. going out with your mates. And leave the competing until you're older and more able to fully commit yourself to the regiment that is required for success.

JAMIE CAMERON

MR NEW ZEALAND

JAMIE CAMERON AT THE PECK DECK

Jamie is the ultimate "cool" body builder. In the 4 years that I have known him, I have never once seen him be upset, stressed or have a bad word to say about anyone. He is easy-going, popular, approachable and lives life to the full. Here's his story:

My name is Jamie Cameron. I was born 6th November 1975 in Christchurch, New Zealand.

My height is 176cm and my weight Off Season 109kgs; competition weight is 95kgs.

I played soccer from the age of 7 till 17 and played rugby league for 2 years. I got into body building because I wanted to be better at rugby. Had to be bigger to compete against Island boys living in NZ. I started bodybuilding at the age of 19.

After a year of training I started noticing that my body was growing. After 4 years my physio persuaded me to do my first competition.

MY ACHIEVEMENTS ARE AS FOLLOWS:

1998-NABBA, Auckland champs:
Open Athletic, 2nd place

1998-NABBA, NZ Nationals, Open Athletic:
2nd place

1999-NABBA, Bay of Plenty champs, Physique:
1st place and Overall 1st place

1999-NABBA, NZ Nationals, Physique:
1st place and Overall 1st place

2000-NABBA, North Harbour Champs, Physique:
2nd place

2000-WABBA World Champs, NZ bodybuilding team:
Open Physic, 12th place!!!!

2004-NABBA, Christchurch Classic:
2nd place

2004-EFBB British qualifier, Under 90 kg:
2nd place

2004-NABBA, NZ Nationals, Open Physique:
1st place and Overall 1st place

JAMIE AND MARK CAMERON, TOP COMPETITORS

MR NEW ZEALAND 2004

A FEW WEEKS OUT FROM COMPETITION

I try to stay within 10kgs of my competition weight year round. As I see no point packing on fat, off season, then kill yourself trying to cut up before a show.

Favourite body part: arms.

Favourite training day: legs.

Worst body part: none.

Worst training day: legs
(because I train them until I throw up).

Favourite training method: supersets and giant sets.

I change my training program from week to week, changing sets, reps, exercises to keep my body guessing. Every month I do a week of 50-100 reps on any body part I feel is lagging behind.

Bodybuilding has never given me satisfaction. As with most bodybuilders I am never satisfied with my gains, physique or my achievements. I guess that's what it takes to be a bodybuilder. You have to look at yourself objectively and never be happy, otherwise you will never improve or reach your goals.

To be a champion you have to be prepared to sacrifice everything: food, alcohol, work, relationships, your life is on hold while you're preparing for a competition. If it were easy everyone would look like Arnold. But they don't. Bodybuilding is the hardest sport in the world bar none. It's 24-7.

Bodybuilding is a selfish, lonely sport, there's only room for one person, there is only one goal, to win. Nothing else matters.

Second place is first place loser. Who wants to be a loser? Your body is the only thing you truly own, make the most of it. Train Hard, Train Smart!

WESLEY CLARKE

PRO NATURAL MR UNIVERSE

WES CLARKE, A GENTLEMAN WHO
ALSO HAPPENS TO BE MR UNIVERSE

The first time I met Wes was when he came down for a photo-shoot. He was in great shape and ripped to the bone. Once again, as a great contrast to the exterior, I found Wes a very nice, friendly and down to earth person who spoke softly and articulately. Here is a brief history of Wes by Wes:

I'm Wesley Clarke and I'm a World Natural Bodybuilding Federation (WNBF) Professional Bodybuilder and a Track & Field Athlete (Hammer Thrower and President of Ilford Athletic Club). I am the current WNBF Pro Natural Mr Universe (Heavyweight). I also won this title in 2003. I turned pro in May 2002 on winning the lightweight and overall titles at the BNBF British finals in Edinburgh.

I am a full time Management Accountant at Cope & Timmins Limited who are based in Edmonton, North London. Their main business activity is distribution and manufacture of curtain poles and other window accessories.

It's certainly not easy combining a full time job with both body building and athletics. There never seem to be enough hours in the day so it's a good job that I can get away with 5 hours sleep or less a night! In a typical week I work from 9.00am to 6.30pm Monday to Friday. Monday and Thursday nights are bodybuilding nights so I'm in the gym between 8.00pm and 9.15pm. Tuesday is athletics night so I'm at the track from 7.15pm to 9.00pm. My other training is done on Saturdays and Sundays.

I got into body building more through other people commenting on how good my physique was than through any desire to get up on a stage and compete. Besides, the only exposure I had had to bodybuilding was what I saw on the covers of magazines such as 'Flex' or 'Musclemag' which of course never appealed to me (and I still don't understand why anyone would want to look that un-naturally big). I first became aware of natural bodybuilding in 2000 and having seen a picture of a natural champion endorsing supplements in Flex magazine, I realised that with some additional weight training I could potentially be competitive in that sport.

I've always been a very shy person so moving into the 'showy' world of bodybuilding was quite a big step for me. It has been worthwhile though because it's enabled me to experience a lot of things that may otherwise have passed me by e.g. regular travel to the USA and various media opportunities. It has also given me a little more self-confidence.

I'm a very competitive person so motivation is never a problem for me. I'm always looking to do well in my next competition especially when there's prize money up for grabs. Apart from my athletics coach, no one person motivates me; I just aim to be the best I can be because that's all I can control.

WES IN COMPETITION IN 2004

IN MY OPINION, THE BEST EXERCISES ARE AS FOLLOWS:

Chest – Flat Bench Press

Back – Deadlift

Legs – Back Squats

Biceps – Dumb-bell Curls

Triceps – Lying French Press ('Skull Crushers')

Shoulders – Barbell Military Press

Being a competitive athlete, I stay very lean all year round. I do a lot a general fitness work all year round (e.g. circuit style training, sprinting and plyometrics) and I eat healthily all year round. Over the spring/summer months, I will compete on average around 15 times in Hammer Throwing. For bodybuilding, I need around 4 weeks to prepare for a competition (I got away with 2 weeks for one show in 2004). Preparation involves cutting out complex carbohydrates, increasing the number of gym sessions from 3 to 4 times per week and putting in lots of extra posing practice.

I've had several highlights in my bodybuilding career to date, the best being my second Pro Natural Mr Universe win in June 2004 in Barbados. Despite being defending champion, I genuinely wasn't expecting to win because 2 months earlier I had torn a hamstring and a quad muscle thereby restricting my leg training leading up to the competition. I was also up against Hugh Cotterell from the Cayman Islands who had beaten me 7 months earlier in the WNBF Pro World Championships. Victory was especially nice as Barbados is where my dad is from and is where he now lives.

My strengths lie in doing explosive leg exercises such as standing long jumps and bunny jumps over hurdles. To be honest, I'm not keen on any of the traditional bodybuilding exercises (they're a necessary evil!) but if forced to pick a favourite gym exercise, I would have to say power cleans because that involves an explosive element.

I regard myself equally as an athlete and a body builder and I devote about the same amount of time to both sports. I find that although it's hard training for both, they complement each other quite well.

NATURAL MR UNIVERSE

ROB FEESEY

WORLD LIGHTWEIGHT CHAMPION

ROB FEESEY AT THE NPA

The first time I saw Rob, he had his clothes on and did not look like a body builder. When he took his clothes off, he did not look human! His physique was unbelievable. His conditioning was the best I had ever seen. Rob is another great person who is a superb ambassador to the sport of body building. Let's find out more from Rob:

My name is Rob Feesey and I am a lifetime natural bodybuilder. My titles include ANB Novice Mr GB, three times ANB middleweight Mr GB, two times ANB Pro-Am Champion, ANB Overall British Champion, WFBB Lightweight Champion, EFBB Lightweight Champion, UIBBN World Lightweight Champion.

I am a personal trainer/fitness instructor. I only work part time, basically just enough to make a modest living. Because I work part time I am able to train six days a week. Bodybuilding is, arguably, the hardest and most intensive sport there is. To get to the top you basically have to live it. It is said that bodybuilding is its own reward, however, it would be nice if there were more financial benefits for all our hard work and dedication, especially if you regularly represent Great Britain at an international level.

I got into bodybuilding partly because a muscular fit body is appealing to women and respected by men. It has elevated my self-worth and confidence immeasurably. For me, being happy with the way that you look, coupled with good health, goes a long way towards contentment and lessens the need for external material wants. Remember, you cannot buy happiness.

I am highly self-motivated and need little external reinforcement, however, observing fat people helps! The great ethos of physical culture "a healthy mind in a healthy body" keeps me inspired. There is no better way to live than inside a strong muscular, fit and healthy body.

MY FAVOURITE EXERCISES FOR VARIOUS BODYPARTS ARE:

Chest – dumbbell bench press

Back – chin-ups

Legs – barbell back squats

Biceps – dumbbell twisting curls

Triceps – bar or bench dips

Shoulders – single dumbbell seated presses

My favourite exercise is the barbell back squat. I feel that this pushes the body harder than any other exercise, therefore, is probably the most productive for overall muscle growth.

I train hard and diet hard. Basically, whatever it takes. It usually takes me between eight to ten weeks to get into contest condition and then I just maintain that for the rest of the year.

I would say my best moment so far has been winning the natural World Lightweight title.

Finally, if you want to give someone the best present you can introduce them to weight training. A lifetime of good health is priceless. Learn to develop you body, not your ego.

OUTSIDE AT THE NABBA MR UNIVERSE 2004

COMPETING

94

ROB ON STAGE

MARINA CORNWALL

BRITISH BODYBUILDING CHAMPION

Marina has been an inspiration to hundreds of female body builders. This lady has pretty much won every title in the UK & beyond. Here's her story:

My name is Marina Cornwall and I am currently British Bodybuilding Champion, 2nd in the World and 3rd in Europe. I also have many other titles but these are my achievements for 2004.

I am a full time freelance Personal Trainer and Sports therapist and I currently work within a Fitness First gym in Southampton.

It is difficult to work and body-build at the same time. Because I work within the gym I train, I find people are constantly coming up to me whilst I am training and asking advice about training or diet and unfortunately I am not strong enough to say I am training please do not talk to me whilst I am training or pay me and I will give you all the advice your need as it is not in my nature to do so.

I used to compete in the National Ultra fit championships held in GB. This was 10 disciplines against the clock involving running, rowing, bench press, shoulder press, press ups, sit-ups etc. I was very fit at the time and had a reasonable amount of body definition because the event was involving high repetitions on the weights machines. I was then encouraged by a close friend of mine to have a go at bodybuilding because he thought I already had a reasonable physique through the type of training I had already been doing. He has his own Physical Training centre in Gosport Hampshire and used to compete himself as a bodybuilder. He ran his own shows which were very much family shows and the competition was not a qualifier for a GB shows so very much low key.

Body building has given me more confidence. Unfortunately I was married for 10 years and had a break and my husband went off with someone. I was devastated at the time and I lost a lot of weight and was a nervous wreck. I took it very personally felt there was something wrong with me, why did he want to go off with another woman? I threw myself into my sport and fitness and am now British Champion for the second time! I am a firm believer that something always happens for a reason and you either sink or swim, luckily I am a survivor. My experience has made me stronger as a person and I know what I want and don't want. But having to get up on the stage in front of a lot of people has been the biggest thing to deal with. My first competition, the photographer said I looked like I was going to burst into tears as I did not enjoy that part of it. The dieting and the hard training I did not find hard in comparison as getting on the stage.

But it has taught me to like myself again and change my physique to being the best I have ever been even as a teenager.

I keep motivated by constantly wanting to improve my profile, win the titles and for my sponsors, family and friends to be so proud of me and what I have achieved. Fortunately I have had a lot of media coverage and it is just something else to be recognised for my hard work and determination to the point that everywhere I seem to go I get people saying "you are that famous body builder aren't you... well done you look brilliant".

MARINA ONSTAGE

MARINA COMPETING

Two years ago when I won the British championships previously my father was seriously ill in hospital at the time and I was trying to run my own business, train hard for the championships and was running up and down to the hospital attending to my dad every moment I had. A typical day would be start at the gym at 7.00 am have a gap at 8.00 rush up to the hospital feed my dad, wash him, give him breakfast and then get back to the gym for 9.00 am for my next client, continue on a days work and then re-visit at 9.30 pm at night whilst still trying to fit my training and diet in. I eventually lost my dad in the Aug and went on to win the British in the October feeling if my dad was still alive he would be so proud of me.

People that have been negative to me in the past inspire me... people that thought I would not succeed and guys I trained with that said I had shoulders like a 9 year olds and if I turned sideways I would look like a zip!

MY RECOMMENDED EXERCISES ARE:

Chest – Must be all the compound exercise flat and incline presses

Back – Weighted dips

Legs – Squats and walking lunges

Biceps – Probably preacher curls although we don't have one in our gym

Triceps – Overhead extensions

Shoulders – Standing Military press

My favourite exercises are Walking Lunges, love and hate them because they are so tough but my glutes and legs ache for days and I like that soreness; it makes me feel I have a tough workout even more so when I cannot walk down the gym stairs after I have finished. Ronnie Coleman does them outside his Mr Olympia gym walking up and down the yard and then just drops the bar off his neck behind him...but does not have to worry about making a noise in the gym, eh!

To get ready for competitions, I train cardio every morning pre-contest for approx 30mins/40mins with my LA Muscle Fat-stripper and train my heavy weights session later in the day. I normally only need approx 12/14 weeks dieting as I do not go hugely out of shape off season whereas other people may need 16/20 weeks.

Best moments for me have been winning the British Title twice, knowing you are the best in the Country/or 2nd in the world. It is not until someone says wow that is fantastic... you think and realise how good it is to have that title.

Finally, a message to all athletes and potential bodybuilders ..."Train hard have ambition and determination be a winner and believe in yourself. Stop making excuses and go for it!"

And for all the negative people stop asking me please "when are you going to give up or how much longer are you are going to compete for!" :-)

FLAVIA CRISOS

BRAZILIAN FIGURE CHAMPION

I met Flavia at the Miss Universe contest in 2004. I had never come across a "harder" physique than hers. She had great symmetry, great conditioning and when you talk to her, you realize that she has "soul" and a great outlook on life. She tells us more here:

My name is Flavia Crisos and I am the NABBA Brazilian Figure Champion (last 3 years) and NABBA Ms Figure Universe (2003). I have won many competitions, these are just the most recent ones.

I am a personal trainer and also own my own business... I have a suit store (Brazilian bikinis and gym clothes).

Body building and working is not easy, but training is a pleasure for me... I wake up earlier and also go to the bed late to get the job done.

Because of body building, a lot of people know me in Brazil and it also help me in my personal life and business. Body building has helped me in everything...my job, my friends, my motivation ....more money, opportunity to travel, knowing new persons...

I always want to improve my body...my motivation comes from inside. I have to improve

FLAVIA IN COMPETITION

FLAVIA CLOSE UP

FLAVIA ON STAGE

MY RECOMMENDED EXERCISES ARE:

Chest: dumbbell flyes

Back: hammer pulldown

Legs: lunges

Biceps: Lying dumbbell curls

Tris: rope cable

Shoulders: lateral raises

Lunges are great. I like to feel the thighs and glutes burning...

For competitions, normally I get to keep a good form in the off-season...so in 8 weeks I can prepare for a contest...I train 3 hours a day.

The best moments in my body building life are arriving every day at the gym!

Finally, everything comes from inside...it is very important to keep the balance in the mind...if you have a strong mind... you are a strong person...and with hard working everything is possible...don't have limits when you believe in yourself...

ROB LLOYD

MR UK

Rob is a very likable articulate young man who has achieved more in his teens than most people in their entire lives! Here he gives you an in-depth look into his life so far:

I am Rob Lloyd from Southport, Merseyside in the UK. My numerous bodybuilding titles/achievements are:

Under 18 Mr. Southport: 1998 and 2002

Under 18 Mr. Wigan: 2002

Under 18 Mike Ahearne Fitness Classic: Winner 2002

Under 18 Mr. North West: 2002

Under 18 Mr. England: 2002

Under 18 Mr. UK: 2002

Under 18/Teenage Mr. Britain: 2002

Junior Mr. Wigan: 2004

Junior Mike Ahearne Fitness Classic: Champion 2004

Junior EFBB Mansfield and East Midlands Classic: Champion 2004

Junior Mr. UK: 2004

Top 6 Junior Mr. Universe: 2004

Mr. Wigan Junior Best Presentation: 2002 and 2004

Mr. Southport Overall Best Presentation: 1999

With many more to come!

I used to hold a full time job as I worked in sales and as a gym instructor but presently I just work at nights as a door supervisor so I can concentrate on my training and diet throughout the day.

I find that, with the help of protein powders especially, it is quite easy to body-build and work at the same time. The main thing is being disciplined enough to prepare the meals you might struggle to get during short breaks. When I worked full-time during the day I used to have a few rice cakes, protein powder and maybe a bit of fruit and have solid meals before work, during lunch and then after work. After work was when I hit the gym, so it's all about routine really.

I did find working full-time whilst bodybuilding easy but the hard part was when I started dieting as I would do my cardio session first thing in the morning; go home for a meal then rush to work with my energy levels being low for the rest of the day. As I am now only working nights I won't have this problem anymore, the only thing is you have to make sure to stay with a strict routine as all the free time could make things become sidetracked.

My transition into bodybuilding is a long story, done in stages. The first being that my grandad was very fit, strong and healthy and was well respected and loved by everyone that knew him. His strength was also put to use very practically, doing things that most people wouldn't (or couldn't) normally do and finding many uses for it. I guess I wanted to be like my grandad and have the strength, the practicality and the love and respect of those around me. I also liked the strong person image and everything that came with it, like the confidence, the general feeling of capability etc. I liked the appearance of a muscular physique as opposed to being thin as I am naturally lean it was one body type or the other for me. So that's where the will came from.

ROB ON STAGE

Now what made me take up the training was moving house from Liverpool to Southport, we moved to a big house in a place I didn't know anyone so I decided that I would build a decent home gym. This had punch bags, speedballs, benches, multi-gyms, squat racks – the works. This was my new hobby while I was settling in to the area. So my house move was the second reason and where the muscle came from.

Finally with my newfound muscle a friend had said why don't I enter a show, as he believed I would win it and he didn't want someone he knew to win. I was unsure being only fourteen and knowing nothing about it. He introduced me to a family friend who then introduced me to the competition organiser, who is also a great bodybuilder. He then helped me to get ready for his show and has helped greatly ever since. This is where I became the bodybuilder I am today!

The bodybuilding/weight training has helped me in many ways throughout my life. It has given me new and improved abilities and better physical and mental health. It has helped me with careers and kept me busy and away from trouble. I also believe it has kept me safe and away from trouble as I look less like an 'easy target' and when trouble has arisen I have been more capable to deal with it. It also has helped me no end with my own confidence as I ever have a high opinion of myself but it's hard to be complacent when you're known as Mr. Britain or Mr. UK.

I also feel much better within myself and believe that I am a much better, happier person who is far less complacent and far more positive. It has brought me many good close relationships with people and I have made many new friends and I really enjoy what I am doing. There is also the feeling of achievement from being known as a champion for the rest of my life and having something to make my future grandchildren proud of me to the fact that I have already completed most of my life's ambitions and kept probably the most important promise I have ever made (more on that later).

I keep motivated by many means. The constant desire to improve constantly and the fact that every time I look in the mirror I'm never satisfied with what I see looking back keeps me going. I have a strong urge to be the best I can be and strive to see major improvements in all aspects of my physique and I haven't let myself down yet!

I have had many set backs, mainly from illness and loss of appetite causing severe weight loss, but I always bounce back as I believe I have more titles yet to come and I love the challenge.

The other main thing that keeps me going was the tragic death of my best friend and one of my training partners Paul Preston. We had spent a long time training to compete in the Under 18 class of the NABBA North West in 2002 and I spent ages helping him to prepare, perfecting his posing, routine and going through the whole show process with him. We had two major goals, to qualify for and then place first and second at the Teenage Mr. Britain and to one day compete in Mr. Universe. One week before the North West, Paul passed away and I swore I would keep my end of the promise. I entered every show I could that year finishing with the Teenage Mr. Britain. I was never defeated that year and I dedicated all my titles to Paul.

Into 2004 I returned to competition to qualify for and compete in Mr. Universe so I had fully fulfiled my promise to him. Not only that but I placed in the top 6 of the junior category and with my trophy they announced for him to be remembered and that my award was dedicated to him. Even though I have completed my promise to him I still believe I have more titles left to claim and another British title to add to the list!

Paul is just one of the main people who inspire me. My inspiration comes in many different forms, one of them being from Michael Sullivan who's competition was the first I ever entered and he has helped my development and taught me so much about the sport as well as being a great bodybuilder himself. I would not have accomplished anywhere near as much as I have without his help. My family, friends and all the other people who support me (especially from New Attitude Fitness Centre in Southport) inspire me too. They are always there and the support I receive is amazing. I am also inspired by other great bodybuilders such as James 'Flex' Lewis who has turned out to be a great champion and a great friend.

IN MY OPINION THESE ARE THE BEST EXERCISES FOR EACH BODY PART:

Chest – Incline Dumbbell Press

Back – Bent Over Rows for thickness, Wide-grip Pulldowns in front of the neck for width

Legs – Squats for quads, Stiff Legged Deadlifts for hamstrings

Biceps – Standing Barbell Curl

Triceps – Lying Triceps Extension

Shoulders – Seated Dumbbell Press

SWORD AND ROB

My favourite exercise would have to be squats as they are the most result producing exercise there is and they have a level of intensity that you don't get with other exercises.

To get in shape for a competition I will start approximately 8-10 weeks out by adding cardio at 3 sessions per week in the morning and by cutting luxuries, such as sauce and confectioneries, out of my diet. My main sources of nutrition are chicken, turkey, whey protein, potatoes, rice. Then I will assess my progress constantly and decide whether to make adjustments such as decreasing calories, increasing cardio or altering nutrient intake. Come the week of the show I cut out anything that holds water and increase my water intake dramatically until the evening before the show to help with water retention. I also deplete my carbohydrate stores for 3 days and load up for 3 days using mostly baked potatoes without the skin. Come the day of the show I am ready and just sip water throughout the day and eat a serving of protein and carbs every three hours.

The best moment of my bodybuilding/weight training life is split into two parts. The main part was winning the Teenage Mr. Britain title, as my career bodybuilding goal was to win a Mr. Britain title and also because of the significance to me because of my promise to my training partner Paul. The second part was making top 6 in the Mr. Universe as I hadn't even dreamed of taking part in the competition and I was there completing my promise to Paul and making the top places!

My advice I would give is to keep learning, as there is always something new that can help and seek the advice from the best and reputable sources out there. You can get advice from anywhere but you have to make sure it's good advice!

Dedication and consistency is the key, I had to learn this the hard way but you have to keep making little steps forward rather than two forward and two back again otherwise you might end up with nothing!

Don't look for shortcuts or a 'magic pill'. There is no one secret for becoming a great bodybuilder it all comes from eating right, using the right supplementation, getting enough sleep and training properly.

Always use correct, strict form on all exercises and forget about the weight. Train your muscles, not your ego!

Finally, if you are going to compete, know where you are going. There are two types of competition, 'mainstream' and 'natural'. Natural competitions are drug tested and judged much more on condition and shape whereas the mainstream are not tested and have much larger physiques. The idea here is to know where you want to be heading and don't believe you can look like Mr. Olympia by this time next year! My other point with this one is don't make the decision too hastily and see how you respond to your training first. You never know you might be pleasantly surprised!

PAUL AMOS

2003 EFBB LONDON WINNER, PROFESSIONAL MODEL

As a teenager Paul Amos was a chubby kid who used to get bullied. In his early twenties, he decided to do something about it and took up weight training. He wanted more, maybe to get into modelling, anything to make use of his exceptional physique.

Like many aspiring models, Paul was going through life with no real sense of direction. He had a relatively decent physique, aspirations of modelling and greater things but didn't know how to get his physique into a noticeable shape.

Paul had tried several supplements such as Creatine and had written to a few companies seeing if they could help him. Having seen LA Muscle in Men's Health, Paul wrote to them.

LA Muscle invited Paul to their headquarters and decided to work with him to reach some of his goals. They provided Paul with some of their best-selling supplements.

Paul's physique changed so much in just 3 months that he decided to compete in a muscle building competition, the 2003 EFBB South East qualifier, judged by many to be one of the hardest shows to compete in. Paul wasn't looking like a monster bodybuilder; he looked very good and quite sharp.

Paul wasn't a body builder but he looked lean and knew how to pose and how to "dominate". He entered the SE EFBB and beat 9 other well-built guys in his class to become the 2003 winner.

From there, Paul was offered modelling contracts and has appeared in many adverts in magazines such as Men's Health and on at least 5 different sports web sites. Paul's new physique meant that he got noticed. His confidence grew to new heights and he secured a new job with a high salary.

In 2003, Paul starred in his own video, The Ab Man, which has been one of the UK's most popular training videos.

MODEL AND BODY BUILDER

PAUL CAGED UP, ALTHOUGH NO-ONE
IS MORE FREE THINKING THAN PAUL

ONE OF PAUL'S FIRST PHOTOSHOOTS

PAUL HAS GREAT LEG AS WELL
AS UPPER BODY DEVELOPMENT

FEMALE MUSCLE

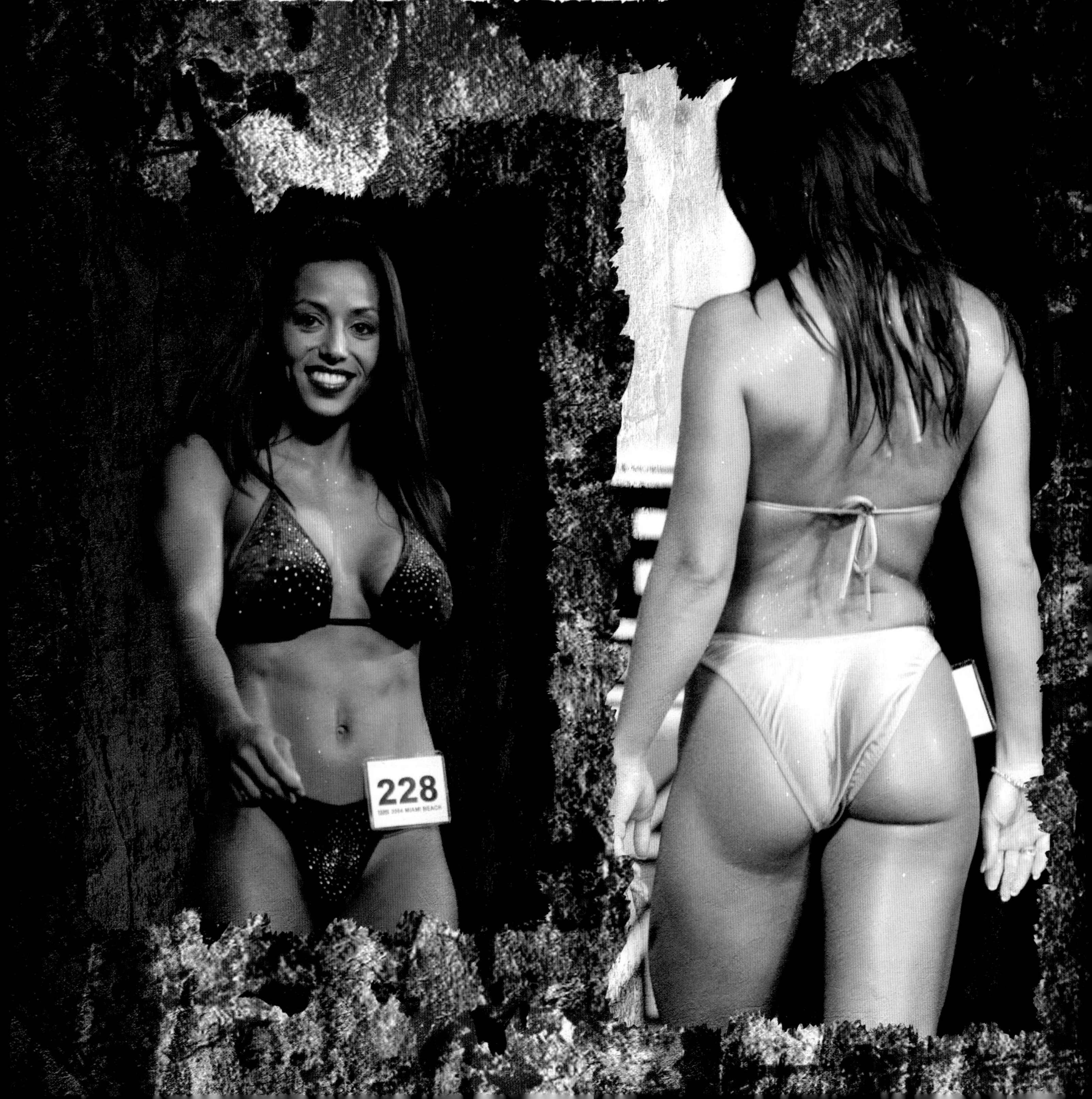
228

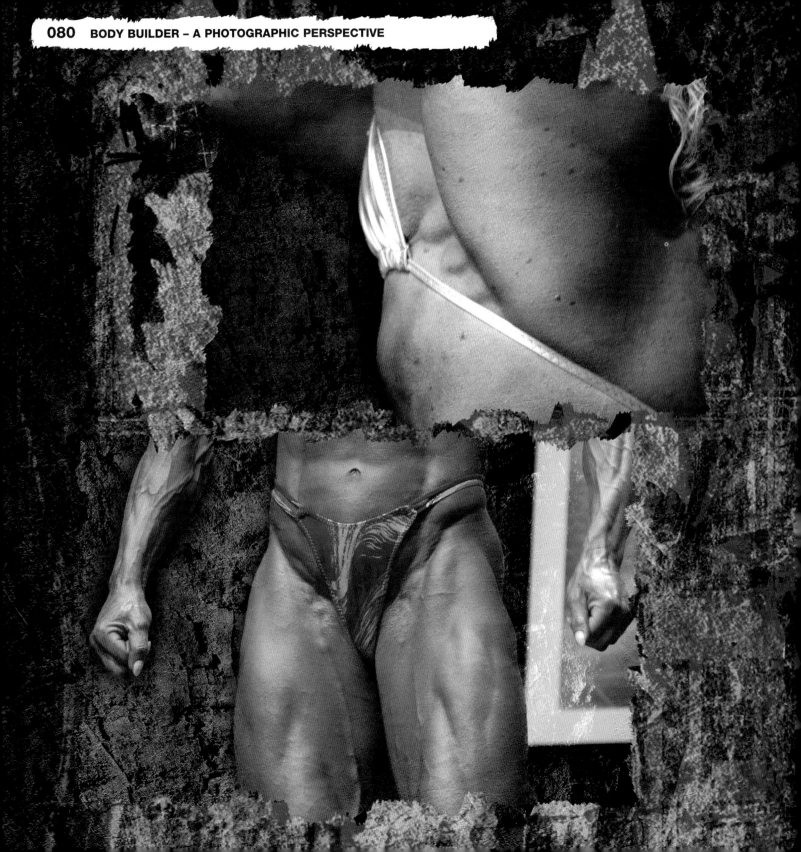

GYM

GETTING READY TO BENCH PRESS

SWORD CURLING WITH SYLVIA SPOTTING HIM

SYLVIA AND SWORD

SWORD, HUSSEIN AND SYLVIA

COMPETITIVE EDGE

COMPETITIONS

FAME COMPETITORS

AT THE ARNOLD CLASSIC

DARREN GUMBS, CARIBBEAN
BODYBUILDING CHAMPION

AT THE MISS UNIVERSE

EFBB SOUTH EAST

BNBF SOUTHERN 2004

EFBB BEEF

ERNIE TAYLOR IFBB PROFESSIONAL
BODY BUILDER

MUSCLEMANIA BODY

NATURAL BODY BUILDING AT ITS BEST

EFBB EAST, POSEDOWN!

BRITISH NATURAL BODYBUILDING
FEDERATION STAGE

SWORD, EFBB & NABBA COMPETITOR

ULISSES JR, THE ORIGINAL POSEUR!

SIMON AND HUNNY, BEST OF BRITISH BEEF

WATCH YOUR BACK HUNNY!

PAUL GEORGE, ALWAYS IN TOP SHAPE

THE ARNOLD CLASSIC, ONE OF THE
BIGGEST BODY BUILDING SHOWS

ULISSES JR, MUSCLEMANIA CHAMPION 2004

SIMON MORGAN

SERWAN AL JAFF

THE BIG BOYS

MARKUS RUHL PLEASING THE CROWD

DUTCH GRAND PRIX

IFBB STAGE

JAMES LLEWELLYN

BIG JAY CUTLER

IFBB GRAND PRIX 2002

PIGGY BACK ANYONE?

IFBB COMPETITORS

IFBB COMPETITION

MARKUS RUHL ONE OF THE BIGGEST BODYBUILDERS

MARKUS RUHL FLEXING

MARKUS RUHL MUSCULAR

SIMON MORGAN TOP EFBB COMPETITOR

IFBB COMPETITION

DEXTER JACKSON, ONE OF THE
MOST SYMMETRICAL BODYBUILDERS

POSEDOWN

RONNIE COLEMAN, MR OLYMPIA

SIZE AND SYMMETRY

ERNIE TAYLOR MEETS HIS MATCH!

AT THE MR OLYMPIA, THE BOYS LISTEN TO ARNOLD SPEAK

HASSAN AL-SAKA, MR UNIVERSE 2004

JAY CHECKS OUT DEXTER'S CUTS

MASS ON STAGE

VASCULARITY ON STAGE

STRONGER THAN MOST MEN HALF HIS AGE

BEATEN TO SECOND PLACE (NOT AGAIN)

BACKSTAGE

JAMES FLEX LEWIS, NABBA QUALIFIER 2004

MISS UNIVERSE 2004

HE PRACTICED THIS ABOUT 100 TIMES!

MUSCLEMAINIA COMPETITOR, MIAMI 2004